S0-BJA-037

Hello, friends! I am Tiptoe the cat! Would you like a yummy treat?

Where are you going, hedgehog? Would you like a cup of tea?

Wow! How deep!
Better climb up into the
boat and sail to shore.

I wear my seatbelt to make traveling safer.

Boing, boing, boing. Jumping is fun, I could do this all day!

La, la, la!
We are pretending to be popstars.

The fence is so high!
I have to stand on a chair
to see over it.

Train coming through.
We can all sit and ride together.

Oopsie. This is not my home. And those are not my bones!

Hi, little fishy. I can swim like you, see?

This snail does not go fast. He moves along just as slow as can be.

The kite is like a large paintbrush in the sky!

What a lovely shiny Christmas tree. Let's decorate it!

Beautiful flowers everywhere. I want to pick them all!

Pretty bird, you have such lovely feathers!

Did I dream this wonderful day? I had so much fun!